Halala Means Welcome!
A Book of Zulu Words

Written and illustrated by
Ken Wilson-Max

David Bennett Books

Africa

South Africa

*To my father Ken –
thank you for my love
of languages and thirst
for knowledge.
K.W.-M.*

First published in the United Kingdom in 1998 by
David Bennett Books Limited
United Kingdom

Text and illustrations copyright © 1997
Ken Wilson-Max
Concept by Ken Wilson-Max
Style and design of all titles in this series
copyright © 1997 David Bennett Books Limited
and Ken Wilson-Max
Ken Wilson-Max asserts his moral right
to be identified as the author and the
illustrator of this work.

Consultants: Paulette Nhlapo
Said el-Gheithy
Centre for African Language Learning.
Mavuso Tshabalala

British Library Cataloguing-in-Publication Data
A catalogue record for this book is available
from the British Library

ISBN 1 85602 256 0

Production by Imago
Manufactured in Singapore

Africa is a big continent where many people live.
South Africa is one of its many countries.
You can see it shaded green on this map.

Chidi and Michael speak English and Zulu.
We tell their story in English and help you
to learn some Zulu words along the way.
Some words will take lots of practise.
Learn how to make the sounds
of the words by reading
'How to say the words'
at the back of this book.
Ask an adult to help you.

Learning a new language is fun.
Enjoy yourself and practise!
You can find out lots more about the
people and language of South Africa
from many books in your local library.
Have fun!

Chidi

Michael

Chidi's **house (indlu)** has a bright blue **door (umnyango)** and **flowers (izimbali)** in the garden. One hot day, Chidi waits for his best friend, Michael.

"Hello **(Sawubona)** Chidi," said Michael.

"I've brought my new **toy car (umgqukumbane).**"

"Welcome **(Halala)** Michael," said Chidi.

Door **Umnyango**

House **Indlu**

Toy car **Umgqukumbane**

Flowers Izimbali

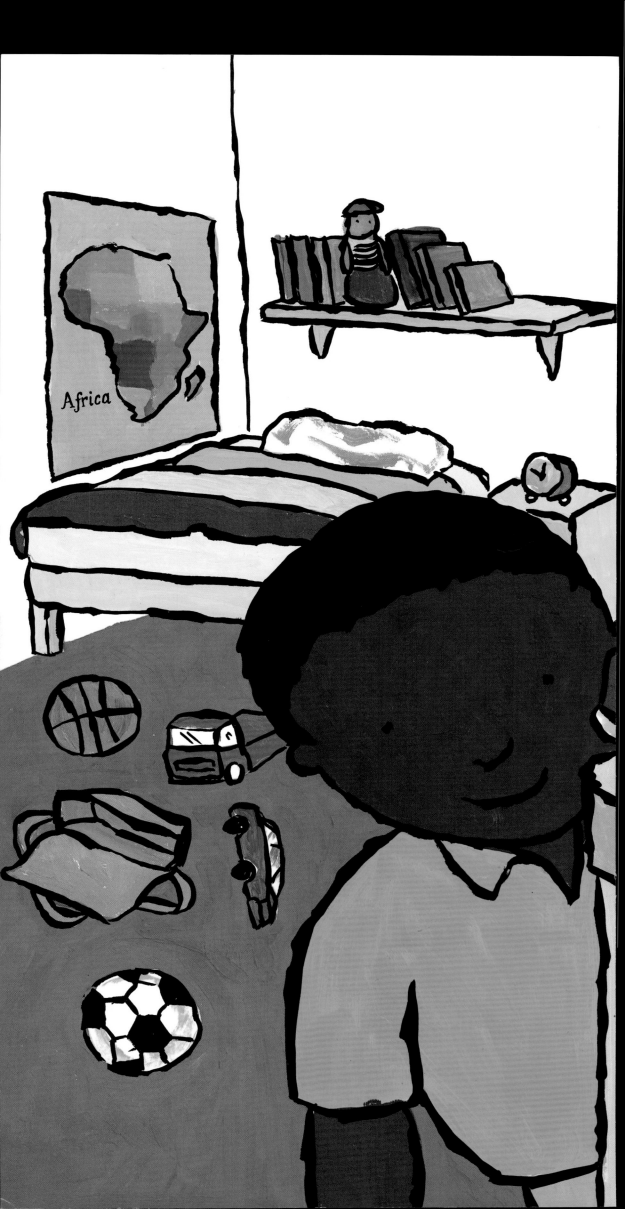

Chidi has a **map (imephu)** and a shelf full of **books (amabhuku)** in his bedroom. Chidi takes the **ball (ibhola)** and the toys from under his **bed (umbhede)**. Then they play with the car from Michael's **bag (umgodla)** on Chidi's **desk (idesiki)**.

Ball **Ibhola**

Bag **Umgodla**

Desk **Idesiki**

Bed **Umbhede**

Books **Amabhuku**

Map **Imephu**

Africa

Mum (Umama) puts two **plates (isitsha)** and a jug of **milk (ubisi)** on the table. Chidi drinks milk from his favourite red **mug (inkomishi)**. Michael drinks a bottle of orange juice.

Mum Umama

Mug Inkomishi

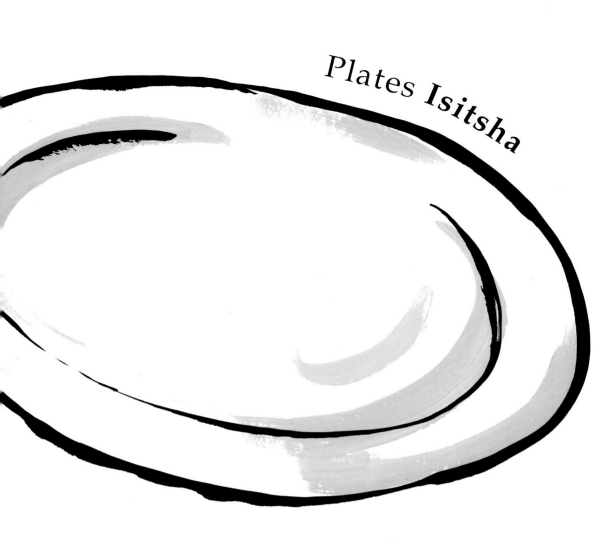

Plates Isitsha

Milk Ubisi

A **hen (isikhukhukazi)** sits quietly on her **egg (iqanda)**. The boys feed the **goat (imbuzi)** and fetch **water (amanzi)** from the **tap (ipompi)** for the **tomatoes (utamatisi)**.

Hen Isikhukhukazi

Egg Iqanda

Goat Imbuzi

Tomatoes Utamatisi

Tap Ipompi

Water Amanzi

The two **friends (abangane)** walk to the bus stop.
"I hope you can come to my house next weekend!" said Michael.
"Goodbye! (Hamba kahle!)" said Chidi as Michael gets onto the **bus (ibhasi).**
"See you next week."
The big **wheel (isondo)** starts turning and the noisy bus pulls away.

Bus **Ibhasi**

Wheels Isondo

Friends Abangane

Goodbye! Hamba kahle!

How to say the words

(Ask an adult to help you with this)

All the words in this book are easy to say if you split the words into single parts. These parts are called syllables. Each syllable has its own sound. Some syllables are called stressed syllables. These are the syllables shown in italics in the word list opposite. They are louder and longer than normal syllables.

Vowels are important in most languages and appear in most words. The vowels are **a**, **e**, **i**, **o** and **u**. They sound like this:
a as in b**a**rk, **e** as in r**ei**gn, **i** as in p**ie**ce, **o** as in b**o**rn and **u** as in r**u**le.

The letter **q**, as in **iqanda** (egg), is said by putting your tongue on the roof of your mouth and clicking it, just like making a tutting sound.

The letters **bh** together sound like a **b**.

Learning new words in any language takes time and practise. Ask people to help you and have fun!

Bag	**Um-*god*-la**
Ball	**I-*bho*-la**
Bed	**Um-*bhe*-de**
Books	**A-ma-*bhu*-ku**
Bus	**I-*bha*-si**
Desk	**I-de-*si*-ki**
Door	**Um-*nyan*-go**
Egg	**I-*qan*-da**
Flowers	**I-zim-*ba*-li**
Friends	**A-bang-*a*-ne**
Goat	**Im-*bu*-zi**
Goodbye	***Ham*-ba *ka*-hle**
Hello	***Saw*-ubona**
Hen	**I-si-khu-khu-*ka*-zi**
House	***Ind*-lu**
Map	**I-*mep*-hu**
Milk	**U-*bi*-si**
Mug	**In-ko-*mi*-shi**
Mum	**U-*ma*-ma**
Plates	**I-*sit*-sha**
Tap	**I-*pom*-pi**
Tomatoes	**U-ta-ma-*ti*-si**
Toy car	**Um-g-qu-k-um-*ba*-ne**
Water	**A-*man*-zi**
Welcome	**Ha-la-la**
Wheel	**I-*son*-do**